Monte's Fur-Ever Friends

Colleen Gilchrist Collins

D1378762

First Printing – February 2022 by CeeGee's Nook Publishing

Text copyright 2022 Colleen Gilchrist Collins
fur.ever.the.momma@gmail.com
Illustrations copyright 2022 Bijan Samaddar

ISBN: 979-8-9853545-1-5

Dedicated to my beautiful mother,
Marilyn Olson Gilchrist, who shared
her love of reading with me.

Special thanks to my loving husband, Joe, for his support and encouragement in writing Monte's story.

A very loud, excited bark was coming from behind the door. Monte was afraid. Monte didn't like loud noises, and he hadn't been around other dogs enough to know if they would like him or not. The Momma picked him up. He trembled and was very alert. He was still afraid of what was on the other side of the door, even when the Momma held him close.

Daddy opened the door and let the loud, ex-cited dog into the room. Daddy had a leash on the other dog and kept him a little way from Monte and the Momma. Monte was afraid.

The Momma lowered Monte to the ground and knelt down beside him. Monte stayed very close to the Momma. Daddy told the excited dog to sit down. The dog stopped barking and sat down. Daddy told the dog that he was a good boy, and he called him Zedd, as he pet the top of his head. Then the Momma told Monte to move a little closer. Monte did. He sniffed the Zedd dog. He smelled like the Momma. She must have held him, too. Maybe Zedd wouldn't hurt Monte. Monte felt hopeful.

Zedd was so excited to see Monte. He wanted to play, but Monte didn't know how. Zedd had a tennis ball in his mouth. He dropped it by Monte's feet. Monte just looked at Zedd. Zedd picked the tennis ball up and brought it to the Momma. She threw the ball, just like she had thrown Monte's lambie toy. Zedd ran after the ball and happily brought it back to the Momma. She threw it. Zedd wagged his tail and ran after it again. Momma told Zedd he was a good boy when he brought the ball back to her.

Monte wanted to be a good boy, too. He brought his lambie toy to the Momma. She threw it, just like she had done with Zedd's tennis ball. Monte ran after the lambie toy and brought it back to the Momma. She threw it again. Monte ran after it. When he brought it back to the Momma, she called him a good boy and pet his head. Monte felt very happy. He liked being a good boy!

Zedd brought the tennis ball to Monte and nudged it toward him with his nose. Monte nudged his lambie toy toward Zedd with his own nose. They played with their toys, and chased each other until they were very tired.

Zedd lay down on the big soft blanket and fell asleep. Monte watched Zedd sleep. Monte felt himself get very sleepy. He wanted the soft blanket, but Zedd was much bigger than he was, and Monte was afraid. Monte laid his head on the corner of the blanket. Zedd kept sleeping. Monte moved onto the blanket. Zedd still slept. Monte moved close to Zedd. Zedd's fur felt like a soft, fluffy blanket. Monte snuggled close and closed his eyes.

When Monte woke from his nap, Zedd was staring at him with a big silly grin on his face. Monte smiled. He had made a friend, and he felt very happy.

Monte and Zedd were playing, when all of a sudden there was a very loud noise. Monte ran and hid under the big bed that the Momma slept in. He didn't like the loud noises that came with the rain. Zedd hid, too. He said that the loud noise was called thunder. It wouldn't hurt them, but it was scary when it made it's loud, clapping sound.

The Momma reached down and picked Monte up. She put him under the blankets on the big bed. Zedd jumped up and crawled under with Monte. The Momma stayed close to both boys, and told them they were safe in the blanket fort, until the thunder stopped. Monte had been very afraid, but it helped to have his friend and the Momma with him. He felt just a little bit better about all that noise now.

When the storm passed, the Momma let the boys outside to play. There is a big swimming pool in the backyard. Zedd likes to jump in and splash around. He is a good swimmer! Monte doesn't go by the blue water. He is afraid, and he doesn't know how to swim. Zedd tells Monte to jump in, but Monte doesn't think that's a good idea. He hides behind a pool chair.

The Momma brings a strange jacket out and puts it on Monte. She walks into the water, holding on to Monte in her arms. The Momma lowers Monte into the water and Monte moves his little legs. He doesn't splash as much as Zedd, but when the Momma lets go of him, Monte is able to swim and play with Zedd. What a nice way to spend a hot, sunny day! Monte is happy that he is able to go in the blue water. He likes his new life jacket. Monte feels very proud of himself for swimming!

At dinner time, Zedd tells Monte a lot of fun stories about school and all of the friends he plays with there. Zedd likes snack time best of all! The Momma says it is time for Monte to join Zedd at school. Monte is afraid, but he is also excited to see all the things that Zedd has talked about.

The next morning, the Momma puts Zedd and Monte into the car and drives them to the doggy daycare school. The boys love car rides, and the Momma rolls the windows down so they can flap their ears in the wind, like airplanes.

When they get to the school, Zedd races in and greets his teachers and friends. Monte stays back by the Momma. He is afraid. The Momma talks to the teachers, and they all say hello to Monte. One teacher stays with Monte and the Momma, while the other teachers go to the play area with Zedd and the other friends.

The teacher talks to Monte and sits on the floor. Monte sniffs her hand. She talks softly and is gentle. Monte likes the teacher. The Momma has to go to work, so she hands Monte to the teacher and says good-bye. Monte is sad to see the Momma leave him, and he wonders if she will ever come back. Monte is afraid again.

The teacher brings Monte to the play area and introduces him to the other friends. Zedd runs over and shows Monte the tennis ball he found. He then races off to join a big black dog named Loki, and a brown dog named Charlie. Monte likes the two big gentle dogs and thinks they are nice.

There are lots of toys and ropes to play with. Monte looks for a lambie toy, but doesn't see one. He isn't really interested in playing with the toys, so he just sits and watches the others run around the play yard.

A big scary looking dog approaches Monte slowly. Monte is afraid and tries to hide. The scary dog finds him and keeps coming his way. The big dog isn't wagging her tail, and she doesn't seem very friendly. Monte feels very small, and very afraid.

The big scary dog has Monte trapped in his hiding place. Monte cries out when the big dog puts her face right next to his. Then a big wet tongue licks Monte's neck. The big scary dog lays down next to Monte and continues to lick him. He is soak and wet, but no longer afraid. The big scary dog isn't really scary, she just looked that way. The teacher tells Monte that her name is Zahra, and that they will be good friends.

At the end of the day, the Momma comes back and picks Monte and Zedd up. Monte is very tired. He has his own stories to tell now, and he has made many new friends. Monte can't wait to go back to school. Monte is very happy!

Connecting: Some children struggle with making friends. Just like any other skill, learning to make friends needs to be taught. Some children learn very early in life how to do this by examples and opportunities set by their parents, and others need a little extra help to figure it out. It is nice to have a good friend, teacher, or mentor to help with these things. Just like Zedd helps Monte, young children need guidance to learn new things. Little Monte faces these same things as he learns to trust, develop social skills, and find a sense of belonging. New things can be very scary and difficult. Trying new foods, storms, sports, swim lessons, moving to a new house, bringing home a new baby, getting a new daddy or mommy... children have many new experiences as they go through childhood. Some children handle change very well, while others have a more difficult time with things. Monte is one of those dogs who is frightened about everything at first. As he figures things out, and tries new things, he gains a little more confidence and resiliency with each new adventure. Separation anxiety is difficult for some children as they transition to daycare or the school setting. Making friends, learning to play and share, and wondering if their caregiver will return to pick them up at the end of the day can be scary things. Differences in how someone looks or acts can also be cause for anxiety. Monte learns that sometimes things are not as they look, and makes a new friend in the end.

Meet the author

Colleen Gilchrist Collins is a retired special education teacher who worked for over thirty years with emotionally, behaviorally, and socially disabled students. She has a bachelors degree in elementary education, and two masters degrees in the field of special education. In her spare time, she loves to travel, coach, craft, and read. Colleen and her husband, Joe, adopted their sweet little Chihuahua mix when he was just under a year old. He had been on the run, and alone, for over three months. Monte's name came from a favorite vacation spot called Montenegro. Monte and his parents currently live in Texas.

Meet the illustrator

Bijan Samaddar, is an independent illustrator who has been working as a children's book illustrator for tenure over 15 years and worked on more than 1,000 books. His main interest is to create an amazing world by illustrating children's books in various styles, as he loves to spend time with kids and work for their own world. His dream is to pick up pencil and paper and travel the whole world and work for kids to make this world a better place to live for all creatures.

Monte lives in his fur-ever home
with Joe and Colleen, in Texas.

Zedd lives in Texas with his best
two legged friend, Chase.

Charlie lives in Minnesota with his
adopted parents, Cliff and Marilyn.

Loki and Zahra live in
Wisconsin with their
newly married parents,
John and Paige.

Monte lives in his fur-ever home
with Joe and Colleen, in Texas.

Zedd lives in Texas with his best
two legged friend, Chase.

Charlie lives in Minnesota with his
adopted parents, Cliff and Marilyn.

Loki and Zahra live in
Wisconsin with their
newly married parents,
John and Paige.

Made in the USA
Coppell, TX
23 August 2022

81933966R00036